W9-BZQ-381

# WORLD'S GREATEST PUZZLES

•••••••••••••••••••••••••

## Charles Barry Townsend

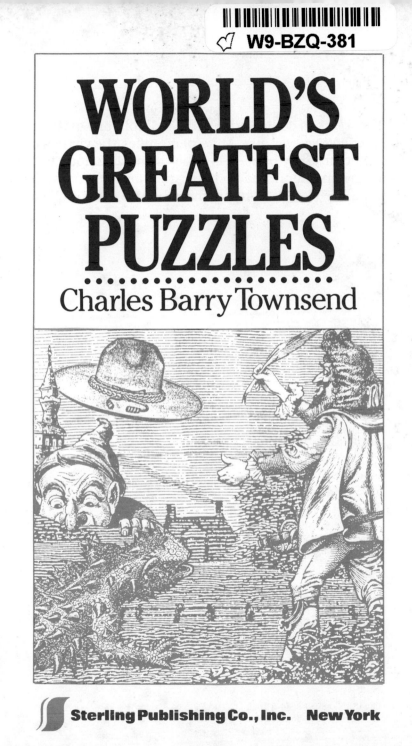

Sterling Publishing Co., Inc.   New York

This book is dedicated to Mike Kristoff, one of the nicest bankers we've ever met. Mike personifies the virtues of the old-time, friendly banker, and he certainly helped to make our stay on Hilton Head Island an enjoyable and memorable one. We wish him many more happy years on Pleasure Island.

**Library of Congress Cataloging-in-Publication Data**

Townsend, Charles Barry.
    World's greatest puzzles / by Charles Barry Townsend.
      p.    cm.
    Includes index.
    ISBN 0-8069-8664-6
    1. Puzzles.  2. Puzzles—History.    I. Title.
    GV1493.T6856    1992
    793.73—dc20                  92-17484
                                          CIP

10  9  8  7  6  5  4  3  2  1

First paperback edition published in 1993 by
Sterling Publishing Company, Inc.
387 Park Avenue South, New York, N.Y. 10016
© 1992 by Charles Barry Townsend
Distributed in Canada by Sterling Publishing
% Canadian Manda Group, P.O. Box 920, Station U
Toronto, Ontario, Canada M8Z 5P9
Distributed in Great Britain and Europe by Cassell PLC
Villiers House, 41/47 Strand, London WC2N 5JE, England
Distributed in Australia by Capricorn Link Ltd.
P.O. Box 665, Lane Cove, NSW 2066
*Manufactured in the United States of America*
*All rights reserved*

Sterling ISBN 0-8069-8664-6 Trade
             0-8069-8665-4 Paper

# Contents

# Introduction

Hello, everybody! Welcome to another round of puzzle solving. This is our sixth puzzle book for Sterling Publishing, and you'll find it every bit as challenging as the earlier ones. As before, we'll be testing all levels of your puzzling abilities. The problems range from downright easy to essentially impossible. Of course, we always supply you with the answers at the back of the book, in case you need a court of last resort.

We've also put together a wonderful and wacky assortment of illustrations to help make each puzzle perfectly clear and understandable. As for subject matter, we have items dealing with dinner plates, matches, chess, baseball, haunted houses, safes, and cigarette makers. Our problems also deal with explorers, lizards, cars, trains, billiards, a hoop gun, playing cards, cryptography, insects and archaeology. So clear your table, sharpen your pencils, and get set for hours of puzzling fun! Our first problem deals with a mystery from the dawn of recorded history. I can hear the stonemasons now, chipping away at the head of the Egyptian puzzle god, Stumpumost the First . . .

# PUZZLES

# World's Greatest "Egyptian" Puzzle

The art of puzzling started in the Valley of the Nile over 3,000 years ago. Here, we see the stonemasons polishing the head of the puzzle god, Stumpumost. The emblem on his helmet is the first recorded line puzzle. To solve it you must draw the jeweled emblem using one continuous line. At no time can you lift your pencil from the paper, nor can you allow the line to cross over itself at any point. Solve this one in five minutes and you qualify to be a scribe first-class.

# World's Greatest "Checkers" Puzzle

Pop Bentley, the colossus of Cracker Barrel Checkers, has just defeated Cy Corncrib for the umpteenth time. Above is the end of the game just before Pop delivered the coup de grace. Can you figure out what his moves were? The white pieces are moving up the board while the black are moving down. Pop is playing the black pieces, and it's his move.

# World's Greatest "Math" Puzzle

$$\frac{3}{3} - \frac{3}{3} = 0$$

Back to your seats, students! Recess is over. Your favorite substitute teacher, Ms. Priscilla Sunshine, is here today to put you through your paces.

"First off, students, I have a short test to see how much you've improved since our last meeting. On the board behind me are four rather ornate 'threes.' You are to arrange these threes, along with any common arithmetical signs, so that they equal, in turn, the numbers 1 through 10. On the board I've given you an example of how you could arrange them to equal zero. You have 15 minutes to finish this test."

# World's Greatest "Plate" Puzzle

Mr Maskelyne makes things spin

Pictured here is that famous 1890s plate spinologist, John N. Maskelyne. He could keep six plates and a washbasin constantly spinning for five minutes or more. Today he has a plate puzzle for you. He challenges you to balance the center of a plate on the point of a needle that has been driven into the top of a corked bottle. You are allowed to make use of four forks and two extra corks to accomplish this seemingly impossible feat. If done correctly, you should be able to emulate Mr. Maskelyne and set the plate spinning after you've balanced it on the pin.

# World's Greatest "Match" Puzzle

*"That was an excellent lunch, Mr. Pettibone. How about a small wager to see who gets to pay for it? I'll bet you can't arrange 15 matchsticks on the table so that they form eight complete squares all the same size. No matches may be overlapped or broken, and no square may be formed inside another. You have until post time to solve it."*

Arbuthnot Longodds, that improver of the breed, is at it again. He never picks up a check if there is a chump handy. Could you solve this matchless puzzle before poor Mr. Pettibone has to reach for his wallet?

# World's Greatest "Chess" Puzzle

Milli Sykes, a waitress over at the Humble Bishop Chess Club, is shown here checking out a puzzle that had everyone stumped last night. Put a queen on one of the corner squares, as indicated above, and see if you can move it through all nine squares in the upper left-hand corner of the board in just four moves. During any one move the queen can traverse as many squares as you want it to but may move in one direction only. See if you can beat the five-minute clock on this one.

# World's Greatest "Betting" Puzzle

J. Wellington Moneybags, the Prince of Gamblers, arrived back in town last night and promptly won a free Blue Plate Special dinner from Griddles Grogan, proprietor of the Bits and Grits Coffee House. Griddles is a sucker for a good bet, and that's just what J. Wellington hit him with. Wellington bet him that he could drop a quarter and a small piece of paper at the same time from a height of four feet and have the paper drop with the same speed as the coin. Nothing else but the coin and piece of paper could be used, and the paper, of course, could not be attached in any way to the coin. As usual, Wellington proved once again that he was the master of the impossible. Can you figure out how he did it?

# World's Greatest "Old Salt" Puzzle

That old seaman, Billy "the Hook" Trelawney, went into Nantucket one day with $10 and came home that night with $150.

He bought himself a new tie at the Tar and Spar Clothing Store and some birdseed for his parrot at the Binnacle Pet Lodge. Later he had his hair cut. Now Billy, who worked at the whaling museum, was paid by check every Thursday. At this time of year the banks were only open on Tuesdays, Fridays and Saturdays. The barber was always closed on Saturday, and the Binnacle Pet Lodge was not open on Thursday or Friday. Given the above facts can you determine which day of the week old Billy went to town on?

# World's Greatest "Baseball" Puzzle

"Batter up!" cries the ump. It's time for the Mudville Nine to take to the field, and it's time for you to fill out your scorecard. What's that? You know the names of the home-town players but you don't know what positions on the team they play! Well, I'm not going to let you off the hook so easily this time. Now listen carefully. I'll tell you some facts concerning each of the players, and it will then be up to you to figure out who plays each of the nine positions on the team. Ready? Here we go:

(1) Andy dislikes the catcher.

(2) Ed's sister is engaged to the second baseman.

(3) The center fielder is taller than the right fielder.

(4) Harry and the third baseman live in the same building.

(5) Paul and Allen each won $20 from the pitcher at pinochle.

(6) Ed and the outfielders play poker during their free time.

(7) The pitcher's wife is the third baseman's sister.

(8) All the battery and infield, except Allen, Harry and Andy, are shorter than Sam.

(9) Paul, Andy and the shortstop lost $50 each at the racetrack.

(10) Paul, Harry, Bill and the catcher took a trouncing from the second baseman at billiards.

(11) Sam has been married for a year.

(12) The catcher and the third baseman each have two children.

(13) Ed, Paul, Jerry, the right fielder and center fielder are bachelors. The others are married.

(14) The shortstop, the third baseman and Bill each cleaned up $100 betting on the fight.

(15) One of the outfielders is either Mike or Andy.

(16) Jerry is taller than Bill.

(17) Mike is shorter than Bill.

(18) Jerry and Mike are each heavier than the third baseman.

You now have all the facts that you will need to determine the names of the men playing all the positions on the Mudville Nine. Play ball!

OUT!

# World's Greatest "Name" Puzzle

One day, while out bike-riding, Mr. Neederwaller chanced to meet a very old friend.

"It's been years since I last saw you," he said.

"I know," replied his friend, "since we last met in Burma I've married—to someone you never knew that I worked with in Rangoon. This is our little girl."

"And a very pretty one at that," replied Mr. Neederwaller. "What might your name be?"

"Thank you, sir. My name is the same as my mother's."

"Well, you certainly look like an Eleanor. That was always one of my favorite names," answered Mr. Neederwaller.

Now, how in the world did Mr. Neederwaller know that the young girl's name was Eleanor? Could he be psychic?

# World's Greatest "Family" Puzzle

Grandpa Townsend used to tell this story. It seems that at one of his birthday parties there were 10 family members present besides numerous other guests. There were two grandfathers present, two grandmothers, three fathers, three mothers, three sons, three daughters, two mothers-in-law, two fathers-in-law, one son-in-law, one daughter-in-law, two brothers and two sisters.

Can you figure out what family members were present at grandpa's party to account for so many family ties?

# World's Greatest "Ghost" Puzzle

> "*Pronounced as one letter, and written with three,*
> *Two letters there are, and two only in me;*
> *I'm double, I'm single, I'm black, blue, and grey,*
> *I'm read from both ends, and the same either way.*"
>
> "*I'm doomed if I can't solve this riddle tonight*
> *To live forever within this terrible site!*"

The ghost of Gregory Quince, for some unknown reason, has been sentenced to haunt Stillwell Grange until he can solve the above riddle. The answer is a very short word. Can you free this shade from his dank imprisonment?

# World's Greatest "Safe" Puzzle

In the annals of crime no petty crook was more petty than Knuckles Halliburton. When robbing a house he never hesitated to steal from the children's banks. Judging by the above picture he must also have been one of the smallest yeggs in history. When he cracked the Security Safe pictured here he took away exactly 100 coins. Their total worth came to $5. There were no nickels in the bank. Can you figure out what coins he came away with and how many of each there were?

# World's Greatest "Prophesy" Puzzle

"All right, Jeffords, I have a little wager for you before the next hand. I'll bet you $1,000, at five-to-one odds, that I can guess closer to the date on any coin that you remove from your pocket than you can. Of course, I get two guesses to your one, but you get to go first. What do you say, is it a bet?"

"Well, High Pockets, that bet sounds pretty good to me, but let's make the odds two-to-one. I guess that the date on the coin will be 1983!"

Even at two-to-one odds this is a cinch bet for High Pockets. How can he be sure that he will win almost every time?

# World's Greatest "Cigarette" Puzzle

Pictured here is that ne'er-do-well of cafe society, Nicotine Ned. It seems that Ned has fallen on bad times and cannot even afford to buy a decent pack of cigarettes. He is forced to roll his own with the help of that famous invention, the Rapide Cigarette Maker. For tobacco, he saves the butts of previous smokes. He can make one cigarette from three butts. Tonight he has saved 10 butts, from which he expects to make five cigarettes. It sounds impossible but Ned has a plan. Can you smoke out his modus operandi?

# World's Greatest "Wedding Gifts" Puzzle

*"I say, Freddy, do you have any idea what wedding gifts we can expect from my uncles?"*

*"Er, well, ah . . . I think that two of them are giving you CHESTY and one of them is giving you CHASTY!"*

Obviously that ardent swain, Freddy Eagerton, doesn't have his mind on Docilla's question. He's inadvertently transposed the letters in the three uncles' gifts. The word "CHASTY" deals with the sea, while the world "CHESTY" is rooted in agriculture. Can you unscramble these words so Docilla can make plans for returning the gifts?

# World's Greatest "Poker Chip" Puzzle

The Mystic Mirror of the Great Gondolpho sees all, knows all, and tells all . . . for $25 a ticket. During his act, the Great Gondolpho illuminates the screen with famous puzzles that he has searched out from around the globe. Pictured here, the Mystic Mirror is projecting the notorious Las Vegas Poker Chip Dilemma. Many a dollar has been lost trying to solve it. The problem is to arrange five poker chips into two rows with one row containing three chips and the other row containing four chips. What makes it a tough bet is that you only have 60 seconds to come up with the answer.

# World's Greatest "Cork" Puzzle

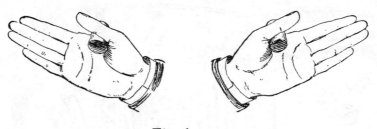

Fig. 1

Fig. 2

Here's a corking-good puzzle you can pop on your guests at your next wine-tasting party. I'm going to let that vintage puzzler from the 19th century, Professor Hoffmann, introduce it:

"Take two wine-bottle corks and hold them as shown in Fig. 1, *viz.*: each laid transversely across the fork of the thumb. Now, with the thumb and second finger of the *right* hand take hold of the cork in the *left* hand (one finger on each end of it) and at the same time, with the thumb and second finger of the *left*, take hold of the cork in the *right* hand and draw them apart.

"The above sounds simple enough, but the neophyte will find that the corks are brought crosswise, as shown in Fig. 2. The puzzle is to avoid this and enable them to part freely."

# World's Greatest "Wagering" Puzzle

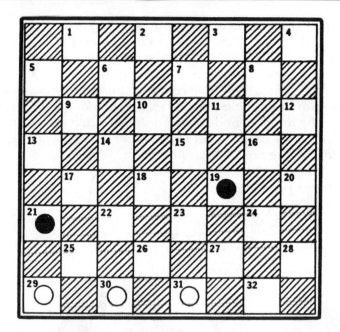

This is called the Double Whammy Wager. You win two times in a row with it. Set up a checkerboard as shown above. Tell your victim that you'll let him have the black checkers—and the first move—and that you'll bet him a dollar that he can't get the black checker on square 19 crowned a king. This looks like a sure thing, but as usual, being a prince of puzzlers, you come out on top.

After he's forked over a dollar, you set the board up again and tell him that now that he knows how it's done you'll give him a chance to win his money back. This time you'll play the black checkers and go first. To his surprise you win again, proving that lightning indeed strikes the same place twice.

The puzzle here is for you to figure out how the above Double Whammy is accomplished. It's easier than it sounds.

# World's Greatest "Explorer" Puzzle

"The situation was certainly dicey, Farquhar, when we reached the river. There were three of us and three native guides whom we were certain would slit our throats and take the golden idols we had found if they could get the upper hand on us. At no time could a single explorer be left alone with two natives, or two explorers alone with three of them. The dugout canoe could only hold two men at a time. How could all six of us get to the other side without losing our lives or the precious artifacts?"

Can you figure out how Livermore safely moved his party across the river and back to civilization?

# World's Greatest "Bear" Puzzle

This problem deals with the one that didn't get away. Our picture shows what happens when a hunter misses his mark. Many miles away, another hunter was more fortunate. He left his camp early in the morning and tracked a bear due south for 10 miles. At this point the bear turned due west and went another 10 miles before the hunter caught up with him and shot him dead. The hunter then dragged the carcass of the bear—it was a small one—back to his camp, a journey of exactly 10 miles. Given these facts can you tell us what color the bear was?

# World's Greatest "Quotation" Puzzle

```
O  F  T  I  Y  G  E
O                    H
N                    T
T                    T
E                    B
                     I
N  V  U  A  G  H  E
```

The jolly tar above invites you to solve a tricky word puzzle. Hidden in the frame above is a famous quotation from America's past. To find it you must go around the frame twice, reading every other letter as you go. Let's see if you can run up the flag before the watch is changed.

# World's Greatest "Planetary" Puzzle

|   |   |   |   |   |
|---|---|---|---|---|
| Q | U | O | T | H |
| L | J | T | S | R |
| R | P | U | A | M |
| I | E | N | R | E |
| T | V | Y | U | C |

Waldo Starfinder, a local amateur astronomer, is checking out our next puzzle. Hidden in the above grid are the names of the nine planets in our solar system plus the name of the star they revolve around. Your job is to spell out the names of these heavenly bodies by starting at any letter and then moving from box to adjoining box either horizontally, vertically, or diagonally. You can re-enter any box after leaving it for another. You have five light minutes to solve this one.

# World's Greatest "Coin" Puzzle

Now, this problem is a real drum-beater. State to your audience that not only can you drop a coin and make it land either heads or tails up on the table, but your hand is so steady that you can make the coin land and stand on its edge from a height of three inches. After the appropriate wagers have been made, you proceed to do just what you said you would. Can you figure out how you're going to win this bet?

# World's Greatest "Horned Lizard" Puzzle

The latest acquisition at our town's nature museum is Balshazzar, a great horned lizard from who knows where. They placed him in a new circular-domed terrarium in our reptile room. Balshazzar immediately set out to explore his new domain. Starting at the door he went due north for 60 inches until he ran into the rim. He then turned due east and scurried straight ahead for 80 inches until he again bumped into the rim of the enclosure. Using these meager facts can you figure out what the diameter of the terrarium is?

# World's Greatest "Number" Puzzle

Back when America hit the road for the first time, competition for business was hot and heavy. It appears that Abner lured them in with puzzles and giveaways. Judging by the difficulty of this problem, I'd say that Abner wasn't losing much money.

Let's see if you'd qualify for a freebie at the lube pit. All you have to do is substitute numbers for the letters in the above math expression. The same number must be used for the same letter. The contest ends in one hour. Good luck!

# World's Greatest "Miscellaneous" Puzzles

"Portia, listen to this in the 'Dear Ariadne' column: 'Dear Ariadne, is it against the law, or the teaching of the Church, for a man to marry his widow's sister?' Is that possible?"

"Land sakes, Pierrepont, you should know the answer to that one. If you want a puzzle to solve, try placing a common mathematical symbol between the numbers 2 and 3 so that you have a number that is larger than 2 and less than 3."

The Partridges are enjoying a peaceful Sunday afternoon puzzling in their new White Mountain hammock chairs. I'd say that the setting up of the chairs would be more of a challenge than the problems that they're working on.

# World's Greatest "Poker" Puzzle

MELVIN    HARVEY

BRUCE    ROLLO

Many years ago, in the old baseball bush leagues, the players would be paid after every game. Many hot poker games ensued into the wee hours of the morning. One such game concerns four players from the Bayside Buzzards. When the game began the four players—Melvin, Harvey, Bruce and Rollo—had $233 between them. When the cock crowed and the game was over, Melvin had $20 more than Harvey, $53 more than Bruce, and $71 more than Rollo. How much money did each of the Buzzards take home that morning?

# World's Greatest "Toy Train" Puzzle

When I was a young lad my dad gave me a set of trains for Christmas. Besides the regular cars that it came with, he bought 20 extra cars for an additional $20. Passenger cars cost $4 each, freight cars were $0.50 each, and coal cars were $0.25 each (this was a long time ago). Can you figure out how many of each type he bought for his $20?

# World's Greatest "Hunter's" Puzzle

"While there are very many as kind as this, they know no task unkind."

No, the old hunter is not talking gibberish, he's just having fun with you. Buried in the above sentence is a piece of good advice. The words of the proverb are in order; you just have to find them. An example of a buried word is: "Where mayhap pleasant flowers will bloom." The word "apple" is hidden in the words "mayhap" and "pleasant." Now, find the proverb, pardner!

# World's Greatest "Punishment" Puzzle

"We are not amused, Master Throckmorton! You will stay after school until you discover a number, written with only odd figures, that is equal in value to an even number. Now, sweep yourself back to the classroom!"

Will Throckmorton ever learn? Mr. Pennypacker has given him tough meat to chew on. He can only use the figures 1, 3, 5, 7, and 9 to make this number. Obviously, numbers like 333, or 753, or 917 are not even numbers. Can you help Throckey get out of detention and out to the baseball diamond?

# World's Greatest "Play Store" Puzzle

"Doris, I'm returning this peach jam. I want a strawberry jam instead."

"Okay, Hally, here's your jam. However, you now owe me an additional 10 cents!"

Hally and Doris are playing store. Hally originally bought three jars of strawberry jam and four jars of peach jam from Doris for $3.10. Now she owes her 10 cents more. From all of this can you figure out the price of a jar of strawberry jam and a jar of peach jam?

# World's Greatest "Word" Puzzle

*"My, what an extraordinary find! According to the local puzzle club there is a five-letter word containing five other words within itself. The letters that make up the word do not have to be rearranged in any manner. Also, each word is complete with no intervening letters. It says that the answer is on page 15, but someone has pinched that section of the paper. I'll be here all day trying to figure this one out!"*

Malcolm Dolittle, prominent young socialite, dropped into his club to relax and found consternation instead. The funny thing is that if you read over his thoughts you'll see the answer as plain as the shine in his hair.

# World's Greatest "Rearranging Bee" Puzzle

NAINWEUEG
ATZAANIN
YKETRU

AMRAIUNAIT
EEDRALNGN
OAIBVLI

NRNGAIEAT
IERGANI
NEEYM

FDNLANI
GOLMANOI
ANITAMSA

It's time for another "rearranging bee"! Listed around the globe above are the names of twelve countries and places. For our test we've scrambled the letters in each name. It's up to you to rearrange them correctly. Fasten your seat belt and start your trip around the world.

# World's Greatest "Bullet Hole" Puzzle

In the lore of the Old West, Cattle Kate was one of a kind. Her prowess with a six gun was legendary. Here we see her winning a bet by shooting 12 bullets into the wall while looking in the other direction. Her bet was that she could line up the holes into seven rows with four holes in each row. Of course, some of the holes would be in more than one row. Sam, the piano man, doesn't seem a bit worried. Where do you think the slugs were drilled into the wall?

# World's Greatest "Car Sale" Puzzle

Well, Daphne, I finally sold that old crock today. I originally priced it at $1,100. When no one was interested I dropped the price to $880. Still no nibbles. I then cut the price to $704. Finally, in desperation, I slashed the price once more and Orvile Winesap came in this morning and bought it. Can you guess the amount he paid for it?

# World's Greatest "Billiards" Puzzle

"Hello, handsome, your name is Bertie isn't it? How about a friendly game . . . of billiards, that is?"

"Er, yes it is, Ms. English. I'm not very good though. Pogston gives me a 25-point handicap whenever we play for 100 points."

"Well, I'll just have to do better than that since I give Poggy a 20-point handicap when I play him. Shall we play for $100 a game?"

From what I've heard of Ms. English's game, I'm afraid Bertie's wallet will be much lighter before this night is over. Can you calculate how many points Ms. English will give Bertie as a handicap before she runs the table on him?

# World's Greatest "Drink Stirrer" Puzzle

DINE and DANCE

Philippe, major-domo of the Glitz and Garter Cabaret, often regales the clientele of this ritzy establishment with puzzles that he has learned during a lifetime of serving the rich and famous. Pictured above is a math equation illustrated with drink stirrers. The expression states that two plus zero equals one. This is, of course, false, but Philippe claims that by moving just one stirrer to a new position the equation can be made to read correctly.

You have until I finish my birch beer to solve this one.

# World's Greatest "Playing Card" Puzzle

Pictured here is an 18th century manufacturer of playing cards. He was certainly a walking advertisement for his product. Back in those days some folks considered a deck of cards an evil waste of time. A deck of cards has many similarities to a calendar. In fact there are at least seven ways in which a deck of cards bears a striking resemblance to a calendar. I'll bet that you can't think of more than five of them.

# World's Greatest "Hoop Gun" Puzzle

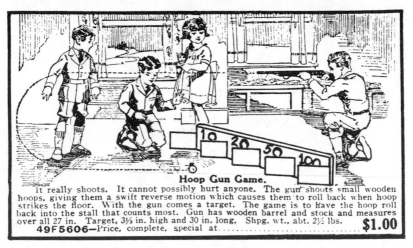

**Hoop Gun Game.**

It really shoots. It cannot possibly hurt anyone. The gun shoots small wooden hoops, giving them a swift reverse motion which causes them to roll back when hoop strikes the floor. With the gun comes a target. The game is to have the hoop roll back into the stall that counts most. Gun has wooden barrel and stock and measures over all 27 in. Target, 3½ in. high and 30 in. long, Shpg. wt., abt. 2½ lbs.

**49F5606**—Price, complete, special at.................. **$1.00**

A great old pastime was the Hoop Gun Game, and it wasn't very expensive either. Here we see Ned Sureshot winning another game from his sister and the Whimpwhiler boys. Ned put 25 straight hoops into the target slots for a total score of 500 points. There are four target slots with point values of 10, 20, 50, and 100. Can you figure out how many hoops Ned placed in each of the slots?

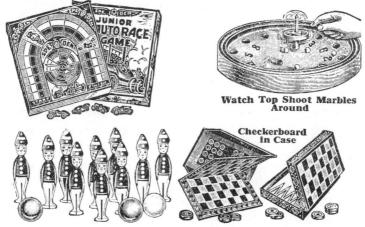

**Watch Top Shoot Marbles Around**

**Checkerboard in Case**

# World's Greatest "Royal" Puzzle

"*I say, Clive, when this rubber is over I have a smashing card puzzle for you. I'd be willing to bet my Bentley against your Rolls that you can't solve it in 30 minutes!*"

Here's how Reggie expects to gain a new car. To solve the puzzle, you have to take the four kings and the four queens and arrange them into a packet that can be dealt out as follows: king, queen, king, queen, king, queen, king, queen. They must be dealt in the following manner:

(1) Take the top card and turn it face up on the table.

(2) Take the next card and place it on the bottom of the deck.

(3) Repeat steps 1 and 2 seven more times.

This is quite a tricky little problem and Reggie just might get to drive a Rolls home. See if you can solve it under 30 minutes!

# World's Greatest "Rebus" Puzzles

"They say that I am a _____ among women!"

"I've seen a lot of _____ down at our pond!"

"Marry me and we will be as snug as _____!"

Complete each sentence with the help of the associated rebus clue.

# World's Greatest "Cryptography" Puzzle

"You intercepted the German High Command's message to their units in Italy and decoded all but the one key word, which would have told us where the counterattack would occur. The code word was E10100010001000UNI100ATXN. Well, Winslow, I translated it and it's an English word. If you were up on your Latin you could have solved it by yourself."

"Confound it, Drummond, spit it out! What's the word?"

Once again Bulldog Drummond has outwitted Scotland Yard. Can you decipher the code word? And what does Latin have to do with it, anyway?

# World's Greatest "Medieval" Puzzle

The scribe pictured here obviously has a penchant for puzzles since he's working through his lunch break compiling the first known work on the subject. His latest entry reads: What number, between 1 and 10, when divided by 4, yields the same answer as when you subtract 4 from it? This strange number is not a whole number since it contains a fraction.

*As recorded by Aloric the Innkeeper on May 1, 973 A.D.*

# World's Greatest "Computer" Puzzle

Our puzzle computer has been grinding away for hours with no end in sight. The problem that it is working on is to take the numbers 1 through 9 and arrange them into three rows where the value of the three-figure number in the middle row is twice that of the number in the first row and the value of the three-figure number in the third row will be three times that of the number in the first row. Let's see if you can beat the number-cruncher to the answer!

# World's Greatest "Birthday Present" Puzzle

Young Maximilian's birthday has rolled around again, and it's time to see if he can't outwit Uncle Otis. Every year Uncle Otis gives Max ten $1 bills and ten $100 bills and tells him to place them into two bowls. Max is free to put any number of bills into each bowl. However, he's not allowed to crush, bend, or fold any of the bills so that he could identify them by touch. Otis then blindfolds Max and moves the bowls around on the table so Max will not know which is which. Otis also mixes up the bills in each bowl in case Max has placed the hundreds on the top. Max is then allowed to reach into one of the bowls and remove one bill, which then becomes his birthday present. It sounds like an even-money bet, but there is a way Max can distribute the bills among the bowls to give himself a far better break on the odds. How does he go about outwitting Uncle Otis?

# World's Greatest "Kissing" Puzzle

"All right, Elvira, let's stop kidding around! Will you give me a kiss if I can prove to you that I can take one away from 29 and have a total of 30 left?"

"Caleb, that's not fair! You know how much I love a good puzzle. Okay, I accept your wager."

Caleb's puzzle is an old, but good one. Do you know how this oily Casanova will win Elvira's lips?

# World's Greatest "Rope Ladder" Puzzle

When the U.S.S. *Extravagantic* pulled into New York Harbor last week it needed some maintenance on its hull. A rope ladder was let down that reached from the deck to the water. The rungs were spaced one foot apart, and there were 50 of them above the water at low tide. The water in New York Harbor rises at about 6 inches an hour. Can you calculate how many rungs will still be above water six hours later when the ocean will be at high tide?

# World's Greatest "Bottle" Puzzle

The following note in a bottle was brought to Professor Flunkum by one of his students. He challenged the learned man to figure out what famous sea captain would have written the poem contained in the note:

"A mighty ship I now command,
With cargo rare from every land.
No goods have I to trade or sell;
Each wind will serve my turn as well;
To neither port nor harbor bound,
My greatest wish to run aground."

Do you know who this poetic pilot was?

# World's Greatest "Glasses" Puzzle

Here's an old-time, after-dinner puzzle from that dean of American puzzlers, Sam Loyd. Line up eight glasses on the table. The first four are empty and the last four are half full of your favorite beverage. You are then required, in four moves, to change the order of the glasses so that every other glass is full. During each move you must pick up and shift two *adjacent* glasses. Solving this problem should take you through dessert and beyond.

# World's Greatest "Ballot" Puzzle

"Get lost, Wolfram, your time has come!"

"Not so fast, your ladyship. I'm a tenured servant protected by the Royal Ballot!"

When King Bowen of Gallstonia died, Queen Olga decided that the time was ripe to fire his manservant, Wolfram, whom she had always hated. However, since he was entitled to the Royal Ballot she had to let him draw ballots to try and hold his job. She placed two folded pieces of paper in her crown. One had "Get Lost" written on it, and the other was supposed to have "Stay" on it. However, the queen wrote "Get Lost" on both slips to make sure Wolfram would be dismissed. In spite of her conniving, Wolfram outwitted the queen and retained his position in the royal household. How did he do it?

# World's Greatest "Addition" Puzzle

Daddy Bruin sounds a little upset over the puzzle he's reading in the *Peltville Gazette*. Let's see what the problem is before he really explodes:

"The row of figures shown here neatly adds up to 45. Can you, by changing one of the plus signs to a multiplication sign and adding one set of parentheses, make this row of figures add up to 100?"

# World's Greatest "Insect" Puzzle

Mr. and Mrs. Firefly are going to be late for the Entomology Ball. Buzzy, their driver, is pushing their puddle-jumper to its limits. When they finally arrive, Buzzy states that he was able to maintain an average speed of 35 miles per hour. Later on that night, on the way home, Buzzy keeps the pace down to a more leisurely, and less bumpy, 25 miles per hour. Can you calculate the average speed for the round trip to the ball?

# World's Greatest "Archaeology" Puzzle

"There it is, Petrie, my greatest find ever. A stone stele from the time of Hammurabi with a Roman math puzzle on it depicted with ancient Babylonian cuneiform figures. I'll be famous!"

"You'll be famous all right, Hawkins," chortled Petrie, "if they don't take away your license to dig. That's the most outlandish fake I've ever seen. Since when did they have a Roman alphabet back in 1800 B.C.? However, the puzzle is a good one. The equation, as it stands, is incorrect. Seven minus two does not equal two. The problem is to move two of the wedges to new positions so that the equation is correct. Let's see if we can solve it."

# World's Greatest "Vacation" Puzzle

"Why, the other day, the maharanee of Pinafore said to me, 'You Americans so love your puzzles. See if you can solve this one: What letter comes next, and why, in the sequence S H O N I X?'"

*Palmas, Calif., July 10, 1902.* Pictured here is that well-known socialite, Ursala Uppercrust of Chevy Glenn, New York, regaling the other vacationers at the fashionable Palm Cliff Hotel with her witty puzzles and stories concerning her many friends around the world. Can you solve the maharanee's problem?

# World's Greatest "Magic Store" Puzzle

Well, here we are at Bland's Magical Palace, that famous Victorian emporium of mystery on New Oxford Street. This is the haunt of the famous puzzle writer, Professor Hoffmann. We're to meet him at 1:00 P.M. Let's go in.

"Hello, professor, we're right on time. Do you have any new puzzles for us today?"

"I certainly do! Please sit down and try your hand at the Three Legacies problem. A gentleman, making his will, left legacies to his three servants. The parlour maid had been with him three times as long as the housemaid, and the cook twice as long as the parlour maid. The gifts were distributed in proportion to the length of service. The total amount to be given out was $700.

"What was the amount received by each of his servants?"

# World's Greatest "Substitution" Puzzle

While the master magician was rummaging through a crate of books, he came across a perplexing math problem that he thought our readers would be interested in. The board he is holding illustrates the puzzle. To solve it you must substitute the digits 1 through 9 for the dots in such a manner that a true mathematical problem is created. There are no zeros, and each digit is only used once. Let's see if you can conjure up the answer in 30 minutes.

# World's Greatest "Bubble" Puzzle

Granddad used to say that one of the great joys of his youth was going to bubble parties. Everyone was given a clay pipe, and prizes were awarded to those who blew the biggest bubbles or who had the most bubbles in the air at one time. When asked what the most bubbles he ever had in the air at one time were, his reply was:

"I'll make a puzzle out of that question, young man!" Granddad loved a good problem. "If I had as many more, and half again as many more, and yet seven more, I should have had 32 bubbles in the air."

From his confusing hints can you figure out exactly how many bubbles he had in the air at one time?

# World's Greatest "Land" Puzzle

Sidney, a local land developer of some renown, is working on plans for a new subdivision. He bought the above 16-acre plot of land, which he intends to divide into 16 one-acre housing lots. The only problem is that the local real-estate ordinance specifies that each lot must be the same size and that every lot must be the same shape as the original 16-acre plot of land.

Can you help Sidney figure out how to lay out the lots so that he can determine what his profits are going to be?

# World's Greatest "Camera" Puzzle

Four avid collectors went to an old camera auction and came home with a bonanza. One of the items on the block was a case containing 233 antique cameras. The collectors pooled their money and made the winning bid. When they got home they divided the cameras up in proportion to the amount of money each of them chipped in.

Flash Farrington received 20 more cameras than Shutters Smollet, 53 more than Wet Plate Pennington, and 71 more than Bellows Barlow. Can you develop an answer to the question, "How many cameras did each of the collectors receive?"

# World's Greatest "Transpositional" Puzzle

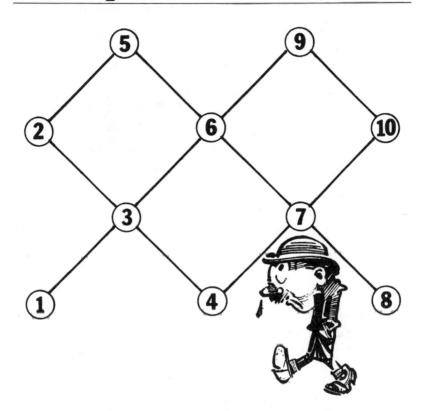

Lonesome George has been going in circles trying to solve this one. Let's help him out. Place two pennies on numbers 1 and 2 and two dimes on numbers 8 and 10. We have to make these four coins change places in just 18 moves. The rules for moving the coins are: You can move one coin at a time to any numbered circle on any straight line. You can move any coin during a turn, but you can't move the same coin twice in a row. The big no-no is that at no time can a penny and a dime come to rest on the same line at the same time.

Those are the rules. You have 15 minutes to solve this puzzle.

# World's Greatest "Carnival Wheel" Puzzle

Jingles, the carnival clown, is right. The boss is a very superstitious man. He always wants the numbers on the wheel, 1 through 11, placed so that any three numbers in a straight line will add up to 18. Can you place them correctly before someone yells, "Hey, Rube?"

# World's Greatest "Train" Puzzle

*"All aboard! New York to Buffalo express!"*

Back in the heyday of the railroads one of the most travelled trains was the New York-to-Buffalo run. Conductor "Tickets" O'Tracy liked to pose the following puzzle concerning that run.

"Every weekday the train left New York at 9 A.M. sharp. Twelve hours later she pulled into the Buffalo station at exactly 9 P.M. that night.

"Now, back in those days, trains would leave from Buffalo for New York every hour on the hour, 24 hours a day. If I were the conductor on the westbound train from New York to Buffalo, how many eastbound trains from Buffalo would I pass from the time I left the station in New York to the time I stepped onto the platform in Buffalo?"

See if you can punch up the answer before we reach Albany.

# World's Greatest "Tips" Puzzle

"Mike, I think that you cheated me when we divided up the luncheon tips!" Pat complained.

"Why, I just thought you were being generous, Pat!" Mike replied innocently.

Here's the problem: After lunch, when they were trying to divide up their tips, Pat gave Mike as many dollars as Mike already had. Mike then said, "This is too much" and gave Pat back as much money as Pat now had left. Pat then said, "No, Mike, this is too much," and gave Mike back as many dollars as Mike now had left. Pat now had no money left and Mike had a total of $80. Pat obviously needs a keeper . . . book, that is. How much money did both waiters have before they started their transactions?

# World's Greatest "Bride" Puzzle

The above none-too-happy-looking bride is the subject of this problem. It seems that she chose wealth before love and is about to pay the price. The following poem concerns her plight. There are four words missing from it which you must discern. The one thing that they have in common is that they are all six letters long and are made up of the same six letters.

"I saw her dance like a _____ upon the green;
Her gown was white, with _____ of yellow dyed;
Her cheeks were like the _____ apple seen.
And now before the _____ she weeps, a bride."

# World's Greatest "Progression" Puzzle

**4, 1, 2 ... ?**

This problem was sent to us by the famous Birdman of Altoona. I just hope that the canary above is cage-broken. Below we have a series of three numbers, 4, 1, and 2. He wants to know the next logical number in the sequence! The answer is one of the following numbers, 6, 7, 8, or 10.

# World's Greatest "Beehive" Puzzle

The bees pictured here are busy trying to rearrange the numbers 1 through 14 in their hive into a more random order. What they are trying to do is to place the numbers in the cells so that no two consecutive numbers are in adjacent cells. And to top it off, no number can be next to a number that divides it evenly. (The number 1 is excluded from consideration.) Try to wax, not wane, on this one.

# World's Greatest "Castle" Puzzle

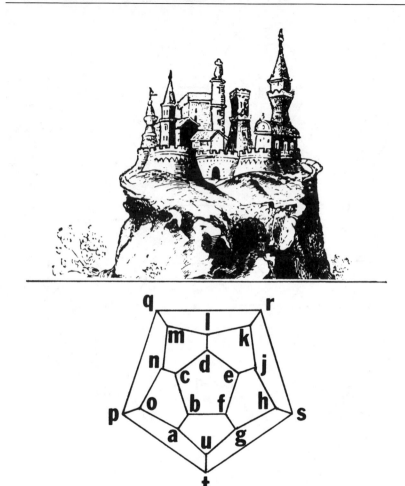

Pictured above is the layout of a mountain castle. The points on the battlements where the sentries are posted are marked with letters. All the posts are connected with walkways, as indicated. What route would the sergeant-at-arms take if he wanted to inspect each post only once during his tour and end up back at his starting point?

# World's Greatest "Marbles" Puzzle

Pictured above is the famous North Jersey shoot-out between "Dutch" Doberman and "Spike" Callahan, back in the summer of 1908. Both players came with bulging marble bags to settle once and for all who had the best thumb in the Oranges. They started the game with the same number of marbles. After the first round Dutch was up 20 marbles. However, on the second and final round, he lost two-thirds of what he had. Spike then had four times as many marbles as Dutch. Can you figure out how many marbles each started with and how many they each had when the game was over?

# World's Greatest "Hidden Word" Puzzles

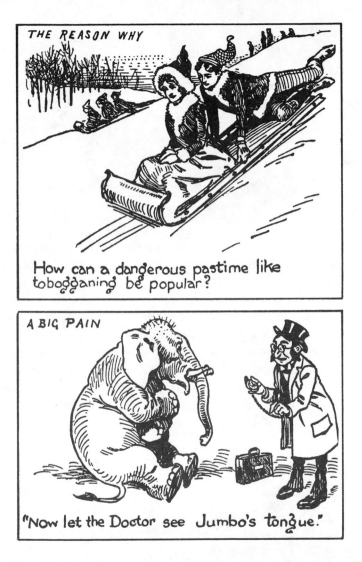

THE REASON WHY

How can a dangerous pastime like tobogganing be popular?

A BIG PAIN

"Now let the Doctor see Jumbo's tongue."

Hidden in the description at the bottom of each picture is the locality of the incident depicted. You have 30 seconds, by the doctor's watch, to find each one.

# World's Greatest "Anagram" Puzzle

"Tonight, Henri, I think I'll have Your Posset and Try Our Steak."

"That sounds good, but I'll have One Solid Lamb and a side dish of Steamed or Tossed."

At the Anagram Club all the dishes are written as anagrams. Can you decode the diners' orders? (Anagrams are words, or groups of words, where the letters have been mixed up to form new words. As an example the word *meals* could be made into the word *Salem*.)

# World's Greatest "Balloon" Puzzle

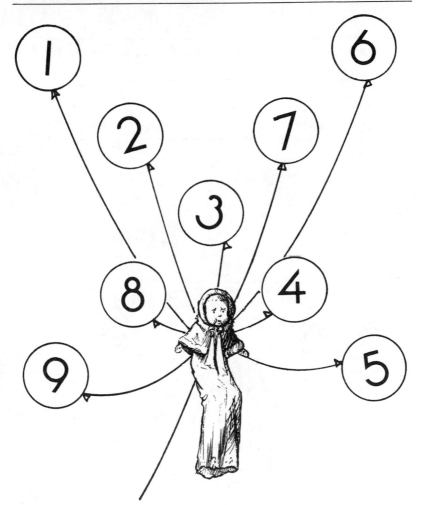

Little Gwendolyn does not look happy about her brother's idea of creative babysitting. However, the numbered balloons remind us of an old puzzle. Can you rearrange the balloons so that the numbers in each of the two rows of five balloons add up to 27? Then tell her brother Pugsley to haul her down.

# World's Greatest "Wine" Puzzle

Here's a puzzle from old Bacchus himself. To get into his party you have to figure out how much wine is in each of two 10-gallon barrels. The barrels are labeled *A* and *B*. Barrel *A* contains more wine than barrel *B*.

First, you pour from barrel *A* into barrel *B* as much wine as barrel *B* already contains. Next, you pour from barrel *B* back into barrel *A* as much wine as barrel *A* now contains. Finally, you pour back from barrel *A* into barrel *B* as much wine as barrel *B* now contains.

At this point both barrels contain 48 pints of wine. How much wine did each barrel contain at the start?

# World's Greatest "Domino" Puzzle

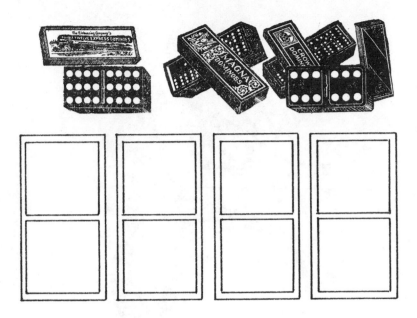

This is one of the few domino puzzles that you are ever liable to run across. Pictured above are four blank dominoes. What you have to do is to figure out where to put 18 spots on them according to the following rules:

The total number of spots on the top halves of the dominoes must be equal to the total number of spots on the bottom halves. Also, the first domino will have twice as many spots as the last domino. One of the pieces has only one spot on it and another one is a double (the top has as many spots as the bottom).

Finally, three dominoes have the same number of spots on their top halves, and two have the same number of spots on their bottom halves.

It sounds confusing, but I bet you can solve it in less than 15 minutes.

# World's Greatest "Nail" Puzzle

Our town's foremost wood butcher, Hiram Ballpeene, is back with another of his "fastenating" nailing puzzles. Hiram has laid out 12 finishing nails to form 4 squares. He challenges you to remove two of these nails so that there are only two squares left. See if you can hammer out the answer in less than 5 minutes.

# World's Greatest "Grid" Puzzle

That famous puzzler, Count de Numburrs, is shown here putting the finishing touches on a classic grid problem. You have to place four sets of the numbers 1, 2, 3 and 4 in the sixteen boxes of the grid in such a way that the same number will not appear in any horizontal or vertical row. This also applies to the two major diagonals. Can you place the final twelve numbers into the grid and solve the problem?

# World's Greatest "Primate" Puzzle

It's lunch time at the local zoo, and down at the primate pavilion the cry is for bananas. Every day 100 bananas are divided up among 100 limb swingers. Each gorilla gets three bananas; each ape gets two. The lemurs, being the smallest, get a half a banana each.

Using these facts to work with, can you figure out how many gorillas, apes and lemurs there are?

# World's Greatest "Television" Puzzle

$$7+7+7+7=100$$

It's four lucky sevens for the Winslow family. They solved the big question on the television show *Family Brood* the other night and won an all-expenses-paid, one-day vacation in Europe. The problem was to rewrite the above math expression, adding only simple arithmetical signs to it, so that the four sevens are indeed equal to 100.

# World's Greatest "After Dinner" Puzzle

Back in the pre-television days when people actually sat around the dinner table and talked, puzzles were a popular form of after-dessert amusement. Here we find "Scissors" Symington showing off his famous Triangle Problem. The puzzle is to take the paper equilateral triangle that he is holding and cut it into five pieces that can subsequently be used to form four smaller equilateral triangles. Not all the pieces will be needed to form each of these triangles. All five pieces are cut in the shape of triangles. I'll have another piece of pie while you're working on this one.

# World's Greatest "Surveying" Puzzle

Peter Plat, the Paderewski of the plumb bob and head surveyor for the Metes and Bounds Surveying Company, has gone back to the books in an attempt to solve this problem. He has to lay out a fence that will exactly divide the above lot into two equal parcels of land, each containing the same number of acres and both exactly the same size and shape. Can you advise Peter as to where this fence should go?

# World's Greatest "Tinsmith" Puzzle

Back in 1776 Timothy of York was the best tinsmith in Boston. As soon as he finishes making the drinking cup he is working on, he's going to tackle a giant puzzle for the owner of the Bloody Marlin Grog Shop down the road. Sitting on the back bench is a large piece of tin that Timothy has to cut into five pieces that can then be arranged to form a perfect square. Can you figure out how he's going to do this?

# World's Greatest "Hot Dog" Puzzle

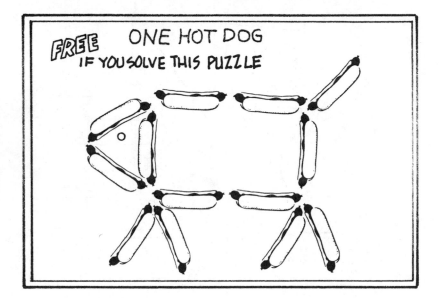

"Hi, kiddies, I'm back with another Murbles stumper. I've arranged 13 hot dogs into a picture of a dog facing west. Can you change the picture so that the dog is now facing east by moving only two of the hot dogs to new positions? The dog must keep his upturned tail. His eye is a quarter, and you can also move that. The first one to solve it gets a Murbles Masterpiece in mustard!"

# World's Greatest "Chemistry" Puzzle

Jimmy: "Hey, Ma! I've done it! I've done it! I just isolated the chemical compound *HIJKLMNO!*"

Mother: "That's nice, Jimmy, don't burn the carpet!"

Well, it looks like Jimmy A. Chiver, the boy wonder of Ashtabula, Ohio, has made a chemical breakthrough. Can you figure out what uses he'll discover for his new compound, *HIJKLMNO?*

# World's Greatest "Boiler" Puzzle

The James Gang is shown here paying another visit to old Number 54. This engine is twice as old as its boiler was when the engine was as old as the boiler is now. The boiler had to be replaced a few years back when the James boys blew it up. The sum of the ages of the engine and the boiler, when this picture was taken, was 49 years. How old were the engine and the boiler at that time?

# World's Greatest "Vitascope" Puzzle

During the early days of the movies, theatres would often have "Puzzle Parties" to help bring in the crowds. Before the movie began, they would flash puzzles on the screen and the patrons would jot down the answers on their programs and hand them in hoping to win something. The puzzle being projected above shows a Roman numeral nine. The problem is to add one line to this figure so that it is turned into an *even* number. Your answer must be a conventional number.

# World's Greatest "What" Puzzles

"What's best when it's cracked?"
"What's the hardest thing to deal with?"
"What key is hardest to turn?"
"What has 18 legs and catches flies?"
"What flowers are kissable?"
"What men have made their mark in the world?"
"What's worse than raining cats and dogs?"

The winners of the Lake Running Bear Middle School "What" contest of 1906.

# World's Greatest "Clock" Puzzle

Here's a picture of J. Wellington Moneybags's famous lucky-dice clock. It never fails to awaken him before an important game. J. Wellington is well known to be able to find betting possibilities in almost any object, and his clock is no exception. He'll bet you that you can't draw two straight lines across the face of the clock in such a manner that the sum of the numbers in each section will add up to the same total. He figures that this is an even-money bet with a time limit of five minutes.

# World's Greatest "Triangle" Puzzle

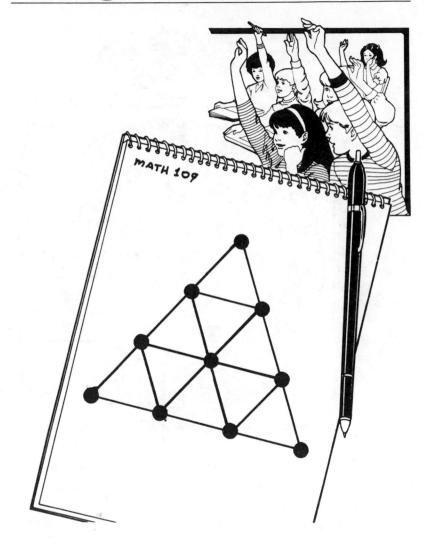

MATH 109

Last night's homework included a geometry stumper. The assignment was to remove four bars from the above drawing so that five triangles remained. Will the teacher see your hand raised?

# World's Greatest "Thinking Cap" Puzzle

| 5 | 11 | 23 | ? | 95 | 191 |

Professor Warwick Barnstable, inventor of the Barnstable Electronic Thinking Cap, has come out of retirement to answer a challenge from the Maplewood Middle School Computer Club. He has donned his famous thinking cap and is attempting to solve the above progression problem before the mighty mites in the background. Can you figure out what the fourth number in the above sequence should be?

# World's Greatest "Somersault" Puzzle

Here's a nice little "gem of the ocean" problem. Pictured here are two Liberty-head silver dollars. They, of course, both have the same circumference. Imagine placing both coins together and pressing down on the tails-up coin so that it cannot move. Now rotate the heads-up coin all the way around the stationary coin until it comes back to its original starting point. How many complete somersaults would the liberty head make during this journey? Would it be one, two, three, or four? Make a guess before you try it with quarters or half-dollars.

# World's Greatest "Spelling" Puzzle

## "_KST_"

> *"Win a free weekend in Altoona, Pennsylvania, by being the first to solve this puzzle: What eight-letter word has the letters KST in its middle, in the beginning, and at the end? Strangely enough, the letters K, S, and T only appear once in the word."*
>
> *"That's easy! Mommy, pack our bags, We're going to Altoona!"*

It looks as though that precocious child, Mehitabel Well-read, the Wunderkind of Wheeling, West Virginia, is headed for the Keystone State. Could you have beat her to the answer?

# World's Greatest "Movie Star" Puzzle

The Dish sisters, Ima and Sucha, were all the rage when they came to Hollywood back in the 1920s. The studio refused to reveal their ages, but a playful press agent teased the reporters with this puzzle.

"Added together, their ages come to 44 years. Right now, Ima is twice as old as Sucha was when Ima was half as old as Sucha will be when Sucha is three times as old as Ima was when Ima was three times as old as Sucha. From that you should be able to tell me how old the women are."

# World's Greatest "Statuette" Puzzle

When Calvin Collectible opened his New Antique Shoppe some 20 years ago, these two statuettes were proudly displayed in the front window. Up until last week, they were still there. Then in two days, he sold the first one for $198 and made a 10 percent profit on it, and then he sold the second one for $198 and took a 10 percent loss on it. Taken together, did Calvin make a profit on the two sales or did he sustain a loss?

# World's Greatest "Missing Letters" Puzzle

**FTFTTTTFFFFSSSSEE＿＿O!**

Biff Wellington, gourmet extraordinaire of the post-Revolutionary period, is shown here well in the lead during the annual Feast or Famine Eating Contest at Fraunces Tavern in New York. Wellington seems to be well ahead of his competition in the chicken-eating event. However, his mouth is so full it's hard to understand what he's saying. Can you figure out what the two missing letters are in the sentence above?

# World's Greatest "Travel" Puzzle

Time out for a short vacation. Where would you like to go? In this hidden-places quiz, we've buried the names of 10 places. There's one hidden in each sentence. We supply the answer to the first one to show you how it's done.

1. He thinks I *am her st*upid sister. (Amherst)
2. Let no woman or man dye his or her hair.
3. His overwrought exasperation filled the enemy with dismay.
4. The wounded were brought in nine vehicles.
5. The calmest man is sometimes made irate.
6. The sale must commence at one o'clock.
7. I should be proud to entertain such a guest.
8. The escaping prisoners crossed the river on a raft.
9. He has my R.N. as a monogram on all his notepaper.
10. He must cross the Atlantic or keep quiet.

# World's Greatest "Antique" Puzzle

Down at the Nothing New Antique Mart, Alex Mercator is chortling over his repeat win in the annual Antique Puzzle contest. Here is the problem he solved:

In the land of Barterall; two oil lamps are worth three irons plus one tennis racket. Twenty-five roller skates are worth three oil lamps plus two tennis rackets plus one iron. Given these facts, how many rollers skates are each of the other three items worth?

# ANSWERS

# Answers

And now for the answers! We've done our best to make the solutions as clear as possible. Occasionally, a puzzle will have more than one solution. When this happens, we try to give you the answer that is most often associated with the problem. Sometimes a puzzle will have so many solutions that it is not practical to give more than one. Thankfully, most problems in this book have only one solution.

**"Egyptian" Puzzle (page 6).**

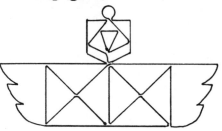

**"Checkers" Puzzle (page 7).** Black to move and win: 27 to 24, 28 to 19, 26 to 23, 19 to 26, and 30 to 16.

**"Math" Puzzle (page 8).** There are many ways to solve this type of puzzle. However, the following ten answers will suffice if you get stuck on any of the numbers:

$$\frac{3}{3} + (3 - 3) = 1 \qquad 3 + \frac{3 \times 3}{3} = 6$$

$$\frac{3}{3} + \frac{3}{3} = 2 \qquad 3 + 3 + \frac{3}{3} = 7$$

$$\sqrt[3]{3 \times 3 \times 3} = 3 \qquad (3 \times 3) - \frac{3}{3} = 8$$

$$\frac{3 + (3 \times 3)}{3} = 4 \qquad (3 \times 3) + (3 - 3) = 9$$

$$3 + 3 - \left(\frac{3}{3}\right) = 5 \qquad (3 \times 3) + \frac{3}{3} = 10$$

**"Plate" Puzzle (page 9).** First, cut the two corks in half lengthwise. Next, force the tines of each fork into a half cork, as pictured below. Make sure that the angle created by each fork and cork is less than 90 degrees. Now place the four corks around the edge of the plate. The forks should be up against the plate edge. This will keep the forks from rocking. You should now be able to balance the plate on the needle point easily.

**"Match" Puzzle (page 10).** This is certainly a different way to solve this type of match puzzle. The diagram shows how to arrange the 15 matchsticks to form eight small squares.

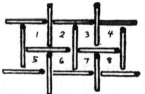

**"Chess" Puzzle (page 11).** To solve this one you have to go outside the nine corner squares, but this doesn't invalidate the solution. You still visit each of the nine corner squares during the four moves of the queen. Try this one at your next chess club meeting.

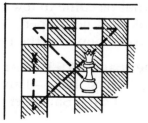

**"Betting" Puzzle (page 12).** The piece of paper must be smaller than the coin. When placed on top of the coin, no part of the paper may stick over any edge of the coin. Hold the coin in your hand by the thumb and first finger. The coin should be parallel to the floor. Place the piece of paper on top of the coin, as shown in the illustration below. When you drop the coin from this position it will fall flat toward the floor. Since no air can get under the paper it will fall to the floor with the same speed as the coin. It rests on the coin all the way to the floor. Give this a try; it really works. You too may be able to win a dinner with it.

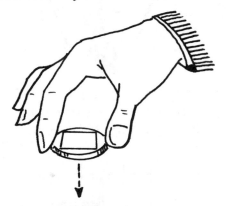

**"Old Salt" Puzzle (page 13).** Old Billy came into port on a Tuesday. In the first place, since the Binnacle Pet Lodge was closed on Thursday and Friday, we have to rule out those days. Next we can rule out Saturday because the barber shop was closed. Since Billy came home with more money than he went to town with, we can suppose that he cashed his paycheck. We know that he was paid on Thursday but since the next two days have been eliminated it stands to reason that he came to town the following Tuesday when the bank was next open. This is also the day when both the barber shop and the Pet Lodge were open.

**"Baseball" Puzzle (page 14).** Pitcher—Harry; Catcher—Allen; Shortstop—Ed; 1st base—Paul; 2nd base—Jerry; 3rd base—Andy; Left field—Sam; Center field—Bill; Right field—Mike.

**"Name" Puzzle (page 16).** Mr. Neederwaller's friend was a lady, not a gentleman, and her name was, of course, Eleanor.

**"Family" Puzzle (page 17).** Grandpa had quite a turnout for his birthday party. The following members, including himself, were present: two brothers and two sisters, their mother and father, and both their mother's and father's parents—the children's two grandfathers and two grandmothers. Ten family members in all.

**"Ghost" Puzzle (page 18).** The word that Gregory Quince is searching for is *EYE*.

**"Safe" Puzzle (page 19).** Knuckles made off with 60 pennies, 39 dimes, and one half dollar.

**"Prophesy" Puzzle (page 20).** High Pockets has the advantage of going second. No matter what date Jeffords picks, all High Pockets has to do is select the next higher and the next lower dates and he will be closer to the date on almost any coin Jeffords removes from his pocket. The only way High Pockets can lose is if Jeffords correctly guesses the date on the coin he removes.

**"Cigarette" Puzzle (page 21).** From nine of the ten butts Ned made three cigarettes. He had one butt left over. After enjoying his weeds, Ned had three new butts. From these he made his fourth smoke. After finishing that one Ned had two butts left, counting the one left over from the original 10. What to do? Ned turned to the table next to his and asked the party there if he could borrow a butt from their ashtray. He now had three butts, from which he made his fifth cigarette. Once he had finished smoking this farewell cigarette he returned the butt to the party he had borrowed it from (why they'd want it back is beyond me) and went home.

**"Wedding Gifts" Puzzle (page 22).** The first word, *CHASTY*, concerns gifts from her two rich shipbuilding uncles, Neap and Ebb Tyde. The gifts are *YACHTS*. The other word, *CHESTY*, is really a gift from her uncle Zeb. It translates to *SCYTHE*, which is probably a reminder to Freddy about the virtues of honest toil as opposed to living off the handsome dowry Docilla is bringing to the marriage.

**"Poker Chip" Puzzle (page 23).** The two rows intersect at one corner. The corner chip has a second chip on top of it. In this way, one row has three chips in it and the other has four.

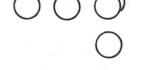

**"Cork" Puzzle (page 24).** The secret lies in the position of the hands as they are brought together. The uninitiated brings them together with the palms of both turned toward the body, with the consequence we have described. To solve the puzzle, turn the palm of the *right hand inward*, and that of the *left hand outward*, in the act of seizing the corks. They will then not get in each other's way, but may be separated without the least difficulty. (From that wonderful 1890s book, "Puzzles Old and New," by Professor Hoffmann.)

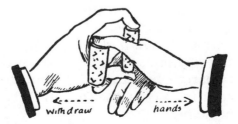

**"Wagering" Puzzle (page 25).** The first win goes like this: The only obvious move for Black is to move from square 19 to 24. White then moves 29 to 25. Black continues by moving 24 to 28. White then moves 30 to 26. Black has to jump 21 to 30 and is made a king. White then moves 31 to 27. Black then has to double-jump 30 to 23 to 32, clearing the last of the white checkers off the board and ending the game before the black checker, from square 19, could make it to the king row.

For bet number two, where you're now playing the black checkers, you make the first move 21 to 25. White then has to jump this checker either going 29 to 22 or 30 to 21. You then move the black checker on 19 to 24. It is now impossible for the white checkers to stop you from eventually moving this checker to the king row and winning your second bet. It's easy when you know how.

**"Explorer" Puzzle (page 26).** Livermore used the following tactics to move his party across the river: (1) Two of the natives were sent over. (2) One native brought back the canoe. (3) The two remaining natives go over. (4) One of the natives brings the canoe back. (5) Two of the explorers now go over. (6) One of the explorers and one of the natives now bring the canoe back. (7) The last two explorers now go over. At this point the three explorers are on the far side with one of the natives. This native is sent back to fetch the other two natives, one at a time.

**"Bear" Puzzle (page 27).** The bear had to be a white polar bear. The North Pole is the only place the hunter could have set up camp where he could go 10 miles south, then 10 miles west and still only be 10 miles away from his camp. That was an easy one.

**"Quotation" Puzzle (page 28).** Starting with the "I" in the lower right-hand corner and reading clockwise skipping every other letter, we get the following nautical quotation: "I have not yet begun to fight." (John Paul Jones, at sea battle, September 1779.)

**"Planetary" Puzzle (page 29).** The planets are: Mercury, Venus, Earth, Mars, Jupiter, Saturn, Uranus, Neptune, and Pluto. The star, of course, is the sun. The illustration shows how to find Venus.

**"Coin" Puzzle (page 30).** To make this work you will need a *straight-sided* glass. Place the glass on the table in front of you and dip the coin you are using in the water. You should perform this puzzle with a dime. Take the wet coin and press it against the side of the glass about three inches above the table. Now, let go of the coin. It will slide down the side of the glass until it reaches the table. The coin is now standing on its edge after you dropped it from a height of three inches. The water causes the coin to cling to the glass as it slides down to the table. All conditions have been met, and the bets are all yours.

**"Horned Lizard" Puzzle (page 31).** This is an easy puzzle. The lizard transversed two legs of a right triangle. When the points of a right triangle touch the sides of a circle the long side, or hypotenuse, of the triangle will be equal to the diameter of the circle. The diameter, therefore, is 100 inches. Remember, the square of the hypotenuse equals the sum of the squares of the two sides of the triangle. (3660 + 6400 = 10,000. The square root of 10,000 is 100 inches.)

**"Number" Puzzle (page 32).** The answer is:

$$
\begin{array}{r}
147 \\
25\overline{)\,3675} \\
\underline{25\phantom{00}} \\
117 \\
\underline{100} \\
175 \\
175
\end{array}
$$

Here's how it's solved: (1) Since the first product is the same as the divisor, the first number of the quotient must be 1. (2) In the second subtraction the letter *E* must be 0 since the letters *FC* are brought down. (3) The letters *FEE* stand for 100. This is the product of *AB* times the second letter, *D*, in the quotient. The divisor does not contain a zero. The only two-digit number when multiplied by a one-digit number that could give a product of 100 is the number 25. So, the divisor is 25 and the second number of the quotient is 4. (4) In the first subtraction, 25 from *GH* gave 11. Therefore, *GH* must be 36. (5) Finally, the last number for *C* must be 7, 8, or 9. If you try each one you'll soon see that only number 7 fits the bill. That wasn't too hard. You're next at the lift.

**"Miscellaneous" Puzzles (page 33).** As far as Pierrepont's problem is concerned, I am sure both the law and the Church frown on a dead man marrying anyone. As for Portia's puzzle, a decimal point between the two and three will yield the number 2.3. This is certainly greater than two and less than three.

**"Poker" Puzzle (page 34).** The money was divided as follows: Melvin had $94.25; Harvey had $74.25; Bruce had $41.25; and Rollo had $23.25.

**"Toy Train" Puzzle (page 35).** He bought the following 20 cars for $20: three passenger cars at $4.00 each ($12); fifteen freight cars at $0.50 each ($7.50); two coal cars at $0.25 each ($0.50). This comes to $12 + 7.50 + 0.50 = $20.00.

**"Hunter's" Puzzle (page 36).** The hidden proverb is: "Let every man skin his own skunk." I guess that's another form of "Everyone should wash his own dirty linen," or words to that effect.

**"Punishment" Puzzle (page 37).** The answer is to use a whole number with a fraction such as 3⅗, which is equal to 4, an even number. Some other examples are: 9%, which equals 10, and 7⁷⁄₇, which equals 8. Batter up!

**"Play Store" Puzzle (page 38).** Strawberry jam costs $0.50 a jar and peach jam costs $0.40 a jar. In the original purchase, three jars of strawberry came to $1.50 and four jars of peach came to $1.60, for a total of $3.10, the amount specified in the problem.

**"Word" Puzzle (page 39).** When he mused ". . .*there* is a five-letter word . . ." he had the answer. The word *THERE* contains: *THE*, *HE*, *HER*, *HERE*, and *ERE*. I hope Malcolm isn't too exhausted working that one out.

**"Rearranging Bee" Puzzle (page 40).** Your trip is over. I hope that you visited all the right places: NAINWEUEG = NEW GUINEA; ATZAANIN = TANZANIA; YKETRU = TURKEY; AMRAIUNAIT = MAURITANIA; EEDRALNGN = GREENLAND; OAIBVLI = BOLIVIA; NRNGAIEAT = ARGENTINA; IERGANI = NIGERIA; NEEYM = YEMEN; FDNLANI = FINLAND; GOLMANOI = MONGOLIA; ANITAMSA = TASMANIA.

**"Bullet Hole" Puzzle (page 41).** After the smoke cleared did you have the following answer?

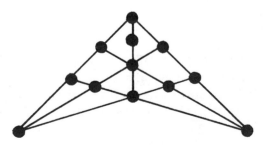

**"Car Sale" Puzzle (page 42).** Since Daphne's hero was dropping the previous price by 20 percent every time he changed it, the final selling price had to be $563.20.

**"Billiards" Puzzle (page 43).** Since Ms. English gives Poggy 20 points in 100, she expects him to make 80 points by the time she makes 100. Poggy thus shoots at a rate of ⅘ that of Miss English. Also, since Bertie is expected to make 75 points for every 100 that Poggy makes, this means that he shoots at a rate of ¾ of that of Poggy. So Bertie must shoot at a rate of ¾ × ⅘, or ⅗, of that of Miss English. That being so, Ms. English will have to give Bertie a handicap of 40 points. She could probably give him 80 points and still win.

**"Drink Stirrer" Puzzle (page 44).** Take a stirrer from the left and place it below the plus sign. The equation now reads: One plus or minus zero equals one.

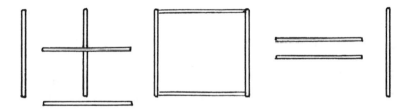

**"Playing Card" Puzzle (page 45).** If all the bets are down I'll show you the seven similarities: (1) There are 52 playing cards and 52 weeks in a year. (2) There are 13 cards in each suit and 13 weeks in each season. (3) There are 4 suits and 4 seasons. (4) There are 12 court (face) cards and 12 months in the year. (5) The red cards stand for day and the black cards, night. (6) If you total up the value of all the cards, counting jacks as 11, queens as 12, and kings as 13, the sum will be 364. Add 1 to this for the joker and you have the number of days in a year. (7) Also of interest: The number of letters in the names of the cards (one, two, three, four, five, six, seven, eight, nine, ten, jack, queen, and king) equals 52, the number of weeks in a year.

**"Hoop Gun" Puzzle (page 46).** Ned scored as follows: 14 hoops in the 10 slot for a score of 140; 8 hoops in the 20 slot for a score of 160; 2 hoops in the 50 slot for a score of 100; 1 hoop in the 100 slot for a score of 100. 140 + 160 + 100 + 100 = 500.

**"Royal" Puzzle (page 47).** The setup of the cards, face down, top to bottom, is as follows: king, king, queen, king, king, queen, queen, queen.

**"Rebus" Puzzles (page 48).** Rebus #1—"They say that I am a *LIONESS* among women!" (LI on S). Rebus #2—"I've seen a lot of *ANEMONE* down at our pond!" (An M on E). Rebus #3—"Marry me and we will be as snug as *TWO PEAS IN A POD!*" (Two P's in a POD).

**"Cryptography" Puzzle (page 49).** The deciphered battle plan word was *EXCOMMUNICATION*. The little bit of Latin needed to solve the puzzle had to do with Roman numerals. Drummond solved it thusly:
(E)(10)(100)(O)(1000)(1000)(UNI)(100)(AT)(X)(N).
(E)(X)  (C)  (O)  (M)     (M)  (UNI)  (C)  (AT)(IO)(N).

The word "EXCOMMUNICATION" made Drummond think of the pope and the Vatican, so his final assumption was that the attack would take place around Rome.

**"Medieval" Puzzle (page 50).** Aloric came up with a good puzzle. The answer is 5⅓.

**"Computer" Puzzle (page 51).** There are at least two solutions to this puzzle:

| 2 | 1 | 9 |
|---|---|---|
| 4 | 3 | 8 |
| 6 | 5 | 7 |

| 3 | 2 | 7 |
|---|---|---|
| 6 | 5 | 4 |
| 9 | 8 | 1 |

**"Birthday Present" Puzzle (page 52).** What Max does is to place one $100 bill in one of the bowls and the remaining 19 bills in the other bowl. He now has a 50–50 chance of picking the bowl with the single $100 bill. However, if he picks the bowl with the 19 bills in it, he has a 9 in 19 chance of picking a $100 bill. So his total chances of winning are: $19/38 + (1/2 \times 9/19) = 19/38 + 9/38 = 28/38$. This means that Max now has a 0.7368 chance—or nearly 74%—of drawing a $100 bill on this and all subsequent birthdays. Now, pass the cake; that puzzle took a lot of effort.

**"Kissing" Puzzle (page 53).** Caleb solved the problem by using Roman numerals. The number 29 is XXIX. Caleb said he would take one away from 29. In this case he removed the I. This, of course, left him with XXX, which is 30. I think this problem isn't worth more than a peck on the cheek.

**"Rope Ladder" Puzzle (page 54).** Since the ship rides up and down with the tide, there will still be 50 rungs above the water at high tide. Did any landlubbers get wet on that puzzle?

**"Bottle" Puzzle (page 55).** The captain, of course, was Noah. He had a large ship with animals from around the world, none of which were for sale. Since there was no land, he didn't care which way the wind blew; all ports were below water. What he wanted most was to find land to ground his ship on.

**"Glasses" Puzzle (page 56).** The glasses are numbered in the illustration. They retain these numbers throughout the moves. The moves are: glasses 2 and 3 to the extreme right end (the performer's right hand); next, fill the gap with 5 and 6; next, fill the second gap with 8 and 2; and lastly finish by moving 1 and 5 to the last gap.

**"Ballot" Puzzle (page 57).** Wolfram figured that the queen would pull a fast one on him, so he did the following: He removed one of the slips from the crown, tore it into small pieces and put them in his pocket. He removed the other piece of paper, opened it up and passed it around for all to see. Since this paper had "Get Lost" written on it, everyone assumed Wolfram's first selection had "Stay" written on it. The queen, of course, could not admit that she had cheated, so Wolfram was able to remain in the palace and serve with distinction for many more years.

**"Addition" Puzzle (page 58).** The answer to this bearish problem is:

$$1 + 2 + 3 + 4 + 5 + 6 + 7 + (8 \times 9) = 100$$

**"Insect" Puzzle (page 59).** On the way to the ball they drove at the rate of 1 mile in $\frac{1}{35}$ of an hour, and on the way home, at the rate of 1 mile in $\frac{1}{25}$ of an hour. Therefore, the average time per mile would be *half* the sum of $\frac{1}{25}$ and $\frac{1}{35}$ of an hour. Finding a common denominator of 175 we come up with $\frac{6}{175}$ of an hour. We can then calculate Buzzy's average speed for the round trip as being $\frac{175}{6}$, or $29\frac{1}{6}$ miles per hour.

**"Archaeology" Puzzle (page 60).** There are at least two answers to this puzzle:

1. $$\text{VII} - \text{II} = \text{V}$$

2. $$\text{VII} - \text{V} = \text{II}$$

**"Vacation" Puzzle (page 61).** The sequence of letters *SHONIX* are the only ones in the alphabet that can be read the same upside down. Therefore, the remaining letter that could be added to this group is *Z*.

**"Magic Store" Puzzle (page 62).** As the amount of each share corresponded with their length of service, it is plain that the housemaid received one share, the parlour maid three, and the cook six, for a total of ten shares. The value of a single share was one-tenth of $700, or $70, which was the portion of the housemaid. The parlour maid received $210 and the cook $420.

**"Substitution" Puzzle (page 63).** The answer is:

$$
\begin{array}{r}
17 \\
\times\ 4 \\
\hline
68 \\
+25 \\
\hline
93
\end{array}
$$

**"Bubble" Puzzle (page 64).** The proof is: Start with 10, add another 10, then add 5, which is half of the original amount, and finally add 7. This comes to: 10 + 10 + 5 + 7 = 32. The answer is ten bubbles. Judging from the picture of the party I'd say that he probably used the balcony to set that record.

**"Land" Puzzle (page 65).** Sidney should subdivide his land as follows:

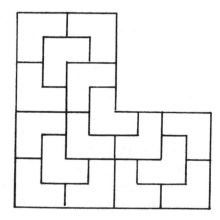

**"Camera" Puzzle (page 66).** The distribution came out as follows: Farrington received 94¼ cameras, Smollet 74¼ cameras, Pennington 41¼ cameras, and Barlow 23¼ cameras. How can you have a quarter of a camera, you ask? What they did was to take the least valuable of the cameras, disassemble it and divide up the pieces among themselves for spare parts.

**"Transposition" Puzzle (page 67).** The moves are: 2 to 3, 8 to 5, 10 to 7, 3 to 9, 5 to 2, 7 to 4, 9 to 6, 4 to 10, 6 to 8, 1 to 6, 2 to 4, 6 to 5, 4 to 3, 10 to 9, 5 to 7, 3 to 2, 9 to 1, and 7 to 10.

**"Carnival Wheel" Puzzle (page 68).**

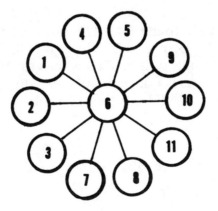

**"Train" Puzzle (page 69).** When O'Tracy stepped off the train in Buffalo he would have passed 25 eastbound trains. The first train he passed was the one just arriving in Grand Central Station at 9 A.M. This is the train that had left Buffalo the night before, at 9 P.M. For the next 12 hours he passed an eastbound train every 30 minutes. He will pass every train that left Buffalo between 10 P.M. the previous night and 8 P.M. that day. That's 23 trains. The train he passed when he left New York made 24, and when he pulls into Buffalo he'll pass the 9 P.M. train leaving for New York, making a grand total of 25 trains.

**"Tips" Puzzle (page 70).** Pat started out with $50 and Mike with $30.

**"Bride" Puzzle (page 71).** The four words are *SPRITE*, *STRIPE*, *RIPEST*, and *PRIEST*.

**"Progression" Puzzle (page 72).** To start with, each number when pronounced can be a word other than a number. Four can be *fore*, one can be *won*, and two can be *too*. Therefore, the one number on the list that can also be a word is *eight*, which is also *ate*.

**"Beehive" Puzzle (page 73).** There are many, many ways to solve this one. If you managed to find one of them it's time to cell-ibrate!

**"Castle" Puzzle (page 74).** There are several routes you could take. One of them is : f, b, a, u, t, p, o, n, c, d, e, j, k, l, m, q, r, s, h, g, f.

**"Marbles" Puzzle (page 75).** The number of marbles Dutch had left is one-fifth the total of all the marbles both boys started with, or two-fifths Dutch's original amount. Dutch's original number, when increased by 20, is six-fifths, and 20 is one-fifth of the original amount. Therefore, each boy started with 100 marbles. When the game was over Dutch had 40 marbles and Spike had 160 marbles.

**"Hidden Word" Puzzles (page 76).** The top is Canada. "How *can a d*angerous pastime like tobogganing be popular?" The second one is Boston. "Now let the Doctor see Jum*bo's ton*gue."

**"Anagram" Puzzle (page 77).** The first order, *Your Posset* and *Try Our Steak* should read *Oyster Soup* and *Roast Turkey.* The second order, *One Solid Lamb* and *Steamed or Tossed,* should read *Boiled Salmon* and *Dressed Tomatoes.*

**"Balloon" Puzzle (page 78).** You can arrange the numbers in several ways. Here's how we did it: One arm is *3, 6, 9, 7, 2;* the other arm is *5, 4, 9, 8, 1.* The 9, of course, appears in both arms.

**"Wine" Puzzle (page 79).** At the start, barrel *A* contained 66 pints of wine and barrel *B* contained 30 pints of wine.

**"Domino" Puzzle (page 80).**

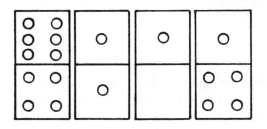

**"Nail" Puzzle (page 81).**

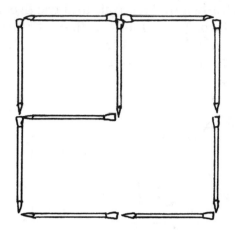

**"Grid" Puzzle (page 82).**

| 2 | 1 | 4 | 3 |
|---|---|---|---|
| 3 | 4 | 1 | 2 |
| 1 | 2 | 3 | 4 |
| 4 | 3 | 2 | 1 |

**"Primate" Puzzle (page 83).** They are five gorillas, 25 apes, and 70 lemurs.

**"Television" Puzzle (page 84).** We are giving you two answers to this problem. There may be more.

(1) $\left(\dfrac{7}{.7}\right) \times \left(\dfrac{7}{.7}\right) = 100$ 　　(2) $\dfrac{77}{.77} = \dfrac{7700}{77} = 100$

**"After Dinner" Puzzle (page 85).** This puzzle is the work of England's greatest puzzle creator, Henry Dudeney. Figure A shows the original triangle and the five pieces that it is to be cut into. Piece 1 is the first of the four smaller triangles. Figures B, C, and D show how the other three triangles are formed from some of the pieces. A very interesting puzzle.

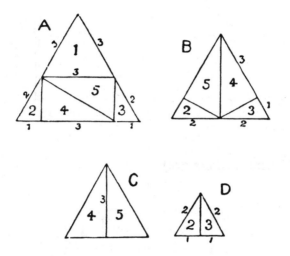

**"Surveying" Puzzle (page 86).** The following drawing shows where the fence is located.

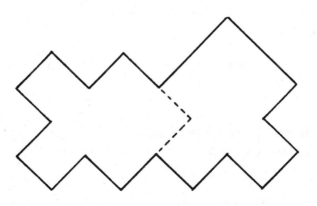

### "Tinsmith" Puzzle (page 87).

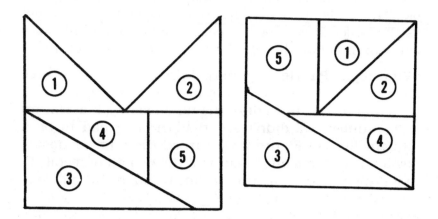

**"Hot Dog" Puzzle (page 88).** The drawing here explains all. Do you want your prize with kraut or piccalilli?

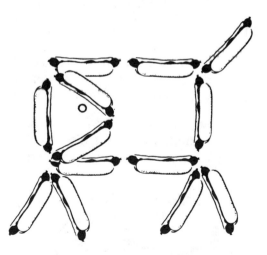

**"Chemistry" Puzzle (page 89).** Jimmy is not about to burn any holes in his mother's carpet, nor will he have any trouble finding uses for *HIJKLMNO*. Jimmy is just having fun with his mother. The compound should be read *H* to *O*, or $H_2O$, or water, since the compound's name is comprised of the letters in the alphabet from *H* through *O*.

**"Boiler" Puzzle (page 90).** When the picture was taken the engine was 28 years old and the boiler was 21 years old. This adds up to 49 years. When the engine was as old as the boiler is now, or 21 years, the boiler was 14 years old, which is half the age of the engine in the picture.

**"Vitascope" Puzzle (page 91).** We've come up with three answers to this puzzle. There may be more. In Figure 1 we've put an "S" in front of the nine making it a *SIX*, an even number. We didn't say that the line had to be a straight line. In Figure 2 we turned the number upside down and added a line, making it the Roman numeral 12. In Figure 3 we drew a straight line through the middle of the number. This makes the top half a Roman numeral 4, and, if you turn the paper upside down, the bottom half a Roman numeral 6.

Fig.1          Fig.2          Fig.3

**"What" Puzzles (page 92).** The answers are: (1) A joke. (2) An old deck of cards. (3) A donkey. (4) A baseball team. (5) Tulips. (6) Those who cannot write. (7) Hailing taxis.

**"Clock" Puzzle (page 93).** The drawing below shows how the clock face is divided. We have three sections with four numbers in each section. The sum of the numbers in each section is 26.

**"Triangle" Puzzle (page 94).** Just remove the bars indicated by the broken lines. You'll be left with four small triangles and one large one. I never said the triangles had to be the same size.

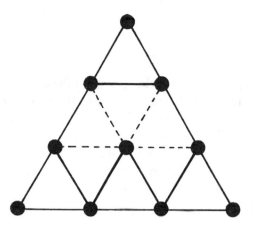

**"Thinking Cap" Puzzle (page 95).** The key to the progression is to double the previous number and add one to it. Thus 2 times 5 plus 1 equals 11, 2 times 11 plus 1 equals 23, 2 times 23 plus 1 equals 47, the answer.

**"Somersault" Puzzle (page 96).** The answer, strangely enough, is *two*. Try it and see.

**"Spelling" Puzzle (page 97).** Mehitabel instantly saw that the answer was the word *INKSTAND*. *KST* appears in the middle. *In* begins the word (the question stated "*in* the beginning") and *and* ended the word (the question stated "*and* at the end"). The answer was really childishly simple.

**"Movie Star" Puzzle (page 98).** This is one hard puzzle! Ima is 27½ years old, and Sucha is 16½. To get the answer, you have to work backward. It also takes a lot of trial and error to arrive at the correct starting ages when working backward. When Sucha was 5½ years old, Ima was 16½. When Sucha is three times that age, she will be 49½ years old. Half of this is 24¾, and when Ima was that age, Sucha was 13¾. Thus, Ima's age is twice this, or 27½.

**"Statuette" Puzzle (page 99).** I'm afraid Calvin took a loss on the deal. His profit on the first statuette came to $18. (Dividing $198 by 11 will give you the 10 percent profit.) However, his 10 percent loss on the second statuette came to $22. (Dividing $198 by 9 will give you the 10 percent loss.) Thus, the $22 loss minus the $18 profit nets a $4 loss overall.

**"Missing Letters" Puzzle (page 100).** What Biff Wellington is doing is counting the number of pieces of chicken that he is consuming. With such a full mouth he seems to be able to get out only the first letter of each word. Since he is counting by fives, the letters stand for *f*ive, *t*en, *f*ifteen, *t*wenty, etc. The two missing letters are *N*, *N*. Thus, the end of the sentence is: *e*ighty-five, *n*inety, *n*inety-five, *o*ne hundred.

**"Travel" Puzzle (page 101).** The *hidden places* are:
1. He thinks I *am her st*upid sister. (Amherst)
2. Let no woma*n or man dy*e his or her hair. (Normandy)
3. His overwrough*t exas*peration filled the enemy with dismay. (Texas)
4. The wounded were brought in *nine veh*icles. (Nineveh)
5. The calmest man is sometimes *made ira*te. (Madeira)
6. The *sale m*ust commence at one o'clock. (Salem)
7. I should be proud to entertain suc*h a gue*st. (The Hague)
8. The escaping prisoners crossed the ri*ver on a* raft. (Verona)
9. He has *my R. N. a*s a monogram on all his notepaper. (Smyrna)
10. He must cross the Atlanti*c or k*eep quiet. (Cork)

**"Antique" Puzzle (page 102).** One oil lamp is worth five roller skates. One iron is worth two roller skates. One tennis racket is worth four roller skates.

# About the Author

Charles Barry Townsend has been writing books on puzzles, games and magic for over 18 years. He is the author of 14 books, including *The World's Best Puzzles*, *The World's Most Challenging Puzzles*, *The World's Toughest Puzzles*, *The World's Most Baffling Puzzles*, *The World's Hardest Puzzles*, and *The World's Best Magic Tricks*, all published by Sterling. He recently moved to Mill Creek, Washington, where he spends a good deal of his time thinking up ways to confound and entertain readers like you.

Pictured below are the author and his dog, Jackie, working on the Checkers puzzle presented on page 7.

# Index to Puzzles and Answers

*Answer pages are in italics.*